FOCUS
on Writing

G000114251

Writing

Introductory Book

**John Jackman and
Wendy Wren**

FOCUS on Writing

Using this book

This book will help you to develop your writing skills to become a really successful writer.

What's in a unit

Each unit is set out in the same way as the example here.

Unit heading
This tells you what you will be learning about

Think about it
Activities to practise, check and develop your writing skills

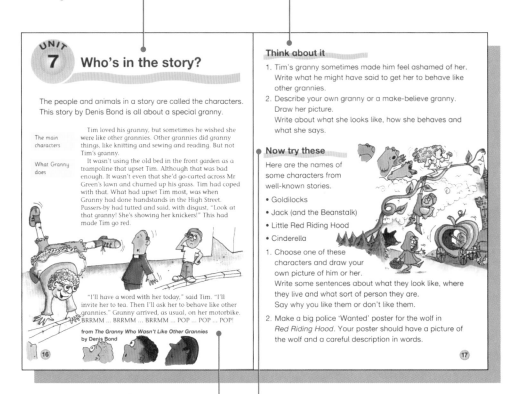

The text
The texts have been carefully selected to demonstrate all major genre types, from fiction to non-fiction. Annotations point out useful techniques and help you to see what really works

Now try these
Activities to stretch and extend your writing skills

Contents

Planning a story

Before we start to write a story, we must think about the order in which things will happen.

The pictures for this story are out of order.
Can you sort them out?

This picture is the beginning of the story

The Bike Accident

Think about it

1. Look at the pictures in order. Write the story of what happened on the bike ride.
   Choose one of these ways to start your story:

   > It was a lovely, sunny day when ...
   >
   > One day Dad and I ...
   >
   > I like bikes, but ...

2. Write a story called 'My Walk to School'. Imagine that something unusual or exciting happened on the way.

Now try these

Finish the sentences, telling what might happen next in each of these pictures.

1.
   Suddenly ...

2.
   After that ...

3.
   Next ...

Writing a story

When we write a story, we need to think about what happens.

In this story, a boy gets lost.

Beginning of the story

Words to use in your story

boy playing parents gone

lost frightened

Words to use in your story

shop assistant helps

End of the story

found safe and happy

Think about it

1. Look at the four pictures.
   Write a story called 'Lost' about what happens in
   the pictures.
   Use the words under the pictures to help you.
2. Write about a time when you were lost.
   It can be a real story, or it can be make-believe.

Now try these

1. This little girl has lost
   her puppy.
   It has run away.
   Write a story about
   the picture.
   Then write about
   what happens next.
   The words in the box
   will help you.

   | walk   park   naughty |
   | lost   run away |
   | crying   calling |

2. Imagine that you have lost something and found it
   again.
   Write about what it was, how you lost it and where
   you found it.
   Make your story interesting by saying how you felt
   when you lost it and how you felt when you found it.

UNIT 3 Writing poems

Writing your own poem is fun!
First, read this poem.

> Two lines in each verse

In come the animals two by two,
Hippopotamus and kangaroo.

> Many rhyming words

In come the animals three by three,
Two big cats and a bumble bee.

In come the animals four by four,
Two through the window and two through the door.

In come the animals five by five,
Almost dead and hardly alive.

In come the animals six by six,
Three with clubs and three with sticks.

Traditional

Think about it

1. Change some of the verses in your own words.
   Don't forget the rhyme. Here is one way to do it:

   In come the animals two by two,
   The big birds walked and the little ones flew.

2. Copy and finish these verses.

   a) In come the animals seven by seven

   b) In come the animals eight by eight.

Poems don't have to rhyme.
Here's part of a poem written by Wes Magee
about when he was young.

Questions ... and answers

> Where's the rattle I shook
> when I was 1?
> *Vanished.*

Three lines in each verse

> Where's the Teddy I hugged
> when I was 2?
> *Lost.*

No rhymes

> Where's the sand-box I played in
> when I was 3?
> *Broken up.*

> Where's the beach ball I kicked
> when I was 4?
> *Burst.*

> Where's the fort that I built
> when I was 5?
> *Destroyed.*

> Where's the box of comics I collected
> when I was 6?
> *Missing.*

> What, all gone,
> everything?
> *Yes, all gone,*
> *all gone ...*

Now try these

1. Write a poem like this about three of your favourite things when you were younger.
2. Copy your poem in your best handwriting and decorate it.

Ordering

When we write instructions, it is very important to put things in the right order.

Here are some instructions for bathing a baby. Would they work?

- Dry the baby with a big towel. Not what you do first

- Put the baby in the water.

- Undress the baby.

- Dress the baby.

- Cover the baby's chest with talcum powder.

Not what you do last - Brush the baby's hair.

Think about it

1. Copy the instructions for bathing a baby, but this time put them in the right order. The first one has been done to help you.

   Undress the baby.

2. You have offered to feed the dog to earn some extra pocket money.
   Write a list of instructions of what to do.
   Remember to do things in a sensible order.

Now try these

1. It was a horrible day outside. You and a friend decided to build a den.
   Describe how you made the den.
   Use these three headings:

   Making a den

   Things we used

   How we built it

   Start by making a list of all the things you used.

2. Draw a picture to show the den.
   Label the drawing to show the main things that you used.

Instructions

You need to be able to write instructions clearly.

Tamsin's mum has invited Yasmin for tea. Yasmin does not know how to get to Tamsin's house. Tamsin gives these instructions to Yasmin.

Each instruction is numbered

1. When you leave the school gate, turn left.
2. Go straight ahead. When you come to St Anne's Road, turn left again.
3. At the end of St Anne's Road is the High Street. Cross at the pedestrian crossing.
4. Turn right and go past the shops.
5. Our road is the next on the left. It is called Ashmore Drive.
6. We live in the block of flats about half way along. It is called Ashmore House.
7. Our flat is number 5, which is on the second floor.

Tamsin also gives Yasmin a map.

A map helps you find your way

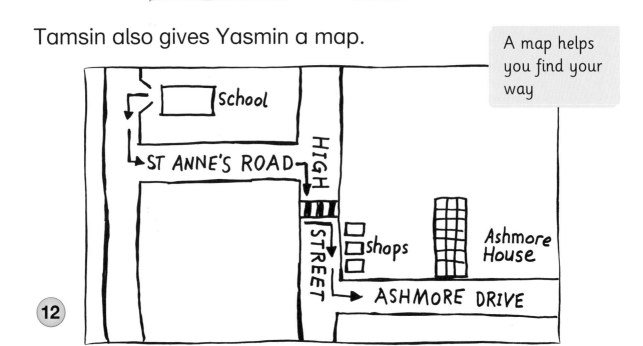

Think about it

1. Your aunt is coming to meet you at school today. Write instructions to show her how to get to school from your home.

2. Draw a map of the route from your home to school.

Now try these

1. A new child has come to your class.
   This child has come from another country, and doesn't know any of the games you play.
   Write instructions to show the new child how to play your favourite game.
   Don't forget to number the stages in the correct order.

2. Your teacher has asked you to help the new child.
   She wants you to write instructions about what you do when you first get to school in the morning.
   Start from when you come into the playground.

Story settings

This is the
setting

Once upon a time there was a little old woman who lived in a small, broken down wooden hut. One day the hairy fairy was passing the door when she found the little old woman talking to herself.

"Oh dear, it's a shame," said the little old woman. "I shouldn't have to live in a small, broken down wooden hut. If only I had a little cottage, with roses around the door, I'd be happy, that I'd be."

The picture
helps to show
the setting

The hairy fairy waved her wand and said, "Very well. Before you go to bed tonight, turn around three times, scratch your head, kiss the cat, and in the morning you'll see what you will see."

So, before she went to bed the little old woman turned around three times, scratched her head, kissed the cat ...

The setting
changes

and in the morning she found that she was in a little cottage, with roses around the door. But the little old woman forgot to thank the hairy fairy.

from *The Hairy Fairy* by John Jackman and Hilary Frost

Think about it

1. Make a list of adjectives to describe the hut and another list to describe the cottage, like this:

Hut	Cottage
old	new
broken down	pretty

2. Imagine that you are in either the hut **or** the cottage. Describe the hut **or** the cottage in detail, saying how you would feel if you lived there.

Now try these

1. What do you think might happen next in the story? Write the rest of the story in your own words.

2. Make up another story about the hut **or** the cottage. Use the list of adjectives you made up before, **or** make a new list if you wish.
   You can have the old woman and the hairy fairy in your story if you wish, but you don't have to.

UNIT 7

Who's in the story?

The people and animals in a story are called the characters. This story by Denis Bond is all about a special granny.

The main characters

What Granny does

Tim loved his granny, but sometimes he wished she were like other grannies. Other grannies did granny things, like knitting and sewing and reading. But not Tim's granny.

It wasn't using the old bed in the front garden as a trampoline that upset Tim. Although that was bad enough. It wasn't even that she'd go-carted across Mr Green's lawn and churned up his grass. Tim had coped with that. What had upset Tim most, was when Granny had done handstands in the High Street. Passers-by had tutted and said, with disgust, "Look at that granny! She's showing her knickers!" This had made Tim go red.

"I'll have a word with her today," said Tim. "I'll invite her to tea. Then I'll ask her to behave like other grannies." Granny arrived, as usual, on her motorbike. BRRMM ... BRRMM ... BRRMM ... POP ... POP ... POP!

from *The Granny Who Wasn't Like Other Grannies* by Denis Bond

Think about it

1. Tim's granny sometimes made him feel ashamed of her. Write what he might have said to get her to behave like other grannies.

2. Describe your own granny or a make-believe granny. Draw her picture.
   Write about what she looks like, how she behaves and what she says.

Now try these

Here are the names of some characters from well-known stories.

- Goldilocks
- Jack (and the Beanstalk)
- Little Red Riding Hood
- Cinderella

1. Choose one of these characters and draw your own picture of him or her.
   Write some sentences about what they look like, where they live and what sort of person they are.
   Say why you like them or don't like them.

2. Make a big police 'Wanted' poster for the wolf in *Red Riding Hood*. Your poster should have a picture of the wolf and a careful description in words.

Making a dictionary

Dictionaries tell us what words mean, and help us to check the spellings.

Here are some words about our bodies from a dictionary.

The definitions

The words

ankle the joint between your foot and leg

brain the grey matter in the skull of humans and animals with which they think

ears the parts on the head through which we hear

elbow the joint between your lower and upper arm

heart the muscle in your chest that pumps blood around your body

knee the joint between your lower and upper leg

lungs the two sacks in your chest that fill with air when you breathe in

muscles the parts of the body that make it move

skeleton the set of bones in the body

skin the outer protective covering of the body

Think about it

1. What are these? Write a definition of each.
   a) ankle   b) elbow   c) skeleton

2. Here are more words about
   your body.
   Copy these words and
   write your own definition
   for each one.

   a) stomach
   b) teeth
   c) tongue
   d) veins

Now try these

1. Here are the names of four buildings.
   Copy the names and write a definition for each one.
   Then draw a small picture next to each one.
   a) school   b) shop
   c) block of flats   d) hospital

2. Write a list of six animals.
   Next to each one, write a definition and draw a
   small picture.

3. Choose another subject you like.
   It could be flowers **or** a sport **or** dancing
   or something else.
   Collect words about your subject and make a dictionary.

Diagrams

Diagrams can often help to explain things.

Here is a diagram that shows how a frog grows from a tiny egg.

How a frog grows

Pictures give lots of information

Numbers help show the order in which things happen

1. Frogs' eggs are called frogspawn.

2. Tadpoles grow inside the jelly.

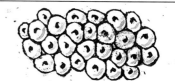

3. The tadpoles hatch.

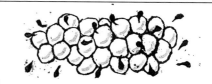

4. They breathe through gills and eat weeds.

5. They grow legs and their tails get shorter.

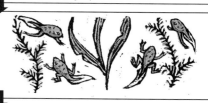

6. The tadpole becomes a frog and the tail disappears.

Think about it

1. Look at the diagram of how a frog grows from a tiny egg, and write the story in your own words. Try not to start every sentence with 'Then ...' Here are some other ways to begin your sentences.

> Soon ...   After this ...   In a short while ...
>
> Once this has happened ...   When ...

2. Make a list of all the machines that people might use in the kitchen, bedroom, living room, garden and garage.

Now try these

1. Here is an explanation of how a bulb becomes a flowering plant.

> 1 Plant the bulb in the soil.
>
> 2 The bulb needs rain and sunshine.
>
> 3 The roots grow down and the shoots grow up.
>
> 4 The bulb plant grows leaves and buds.
>
> 5 The buds grow into flowers.

Draw a diagram to show each step.

2. Make a list of the stages in bathing a dog. Draw a diagram to show each stage.

Writing longer stories

Before we start writing a longer story, we need to think about:

1 What characters will be in the story.

2 Where and when the story will happen.

3 What will happen.

Here is the beginning of a storybook called *Horace*.

Interesting opening sentence ▸

Once there was a cat called Horace who was afraid of the dark. But he kept it a secret, UNTIL –

Characters ▸

Setting ▸

One night Horace's friends Ginger Jones, Short-tail Hansford and Arabella Smith, were playing hide-and-seek by the light of the moon. And they noticed Horace peeping out at them from his kitchen window.

"Hullo, Horace!" shouted Short-tail, "Come and play!"

Horace looked at the dark shadowy garden. "N – n – no thank you," he said. "I – I expect my supper will be ready soon."

Ginger looked at Horace. "You're scared!" he jeered.

"I'm not!" said Horace. "I know cats love to go out at night, and it's all right if they do."

"But you *are* scared!" said Ginger. And he grinned.

Horace couldn't bear it – especially with Arabella listening.

"I'm *not* scared!" he shouted.

"All right!" said Ginger. "Go into the woods – now – by yourself. Go as far as the pond, and get some mud on your paws. Then we'll know you've really been there!"

Go into the *woods*! As far as the *pond*! Horace began to shiver. But Arabella was still listening ...

"All right!" he said. "I'll do it!"

"We'll be waiting!" grinned Ginger.

from *Horace* by Marjorie Newman

Think about it

1. Who are the two main characters in this part of the story of Horace?
2. Where does the story happen? When?
3. What is the story about?
4. What do you think happens next?
   Write the end of the story in your own words.

Now try these

1. Write a story about something frightening, like being in the dark, **or** being lost.
   Before you start, make a plan for your story.
   a) Who will be the characters in your story?
   b) Where and when will the story happen?
   c) What will the story be about?

2. Write your story, then check it and write it again neatly so that other people can read it.

Some poems can also be riddles, and some poems can be funny.

Here are some riddles.
Can you guess the answers?

Answers to riddles can be a surprise

1. I have legs,
   One, two, three four,
   But I cannot walk
   Across the floor.

2. I have teeth,
   Long and white,
   They are sharp
   But I cannot bite.

3. I am round like a ball
   And I live in the sky,
   You will see me at night
   If you look up high.

4. I can prick your finger
   And make you cry,
   But I can't see a thing
   With my one little eye.

Ruth Ainsworth

Here is a tongue twister.
Can you read it quickly? It is hard to say it without making a mistake.

Careful Katie cooked a crisp and crinkly cabbage.
Did careful Katie cook a crisp and crinkly cabbage?
If careful Katie cooked a crisp and crinkly cabbage,
Where's the crisp and crinkly cabbage careful Katie cooked?

Hard to say fast

Here's a funny poem.
It is called a limerick.

A cheerful old bear at the zoo
Could always find something to do.
    When it bored him to go
    On a walk to and fro
He reversed it, and walked fro and to.

Lines 1, 2 and
5 always
rhyme and
lines 3 and 4
always rhyme

Think about it

Riddle poems can be very short.
Copy and finish these.

1. On it I lay my weary head,
   When I go at night to _____.

   What is it?

2. The farmer said I'll show you how
   This white liquid comes from a _____.

   What liquid is it?

Now try these

1. Look at some poetry books and try to find some other
   poems that are riddles or are funny. Choose your
   favourite one and copy it neatly. Try to learn it by heart.

2. Try to write a tongue twister of your own. Start with one
   line of words with the same first letter, then change the
   words around in the other lines.

   You can use nonsense and made up words for fun,
   if you wish.

Writing a report

When we write reports, we must make it easy for the readers to follow our ideas. Here is a report about keeping birds as pets.

Chapter title

Budgerigars and canaries make good pets

Sub-headings

Where they come from
The first budgerigars (or budgies as they are called) were brought from Australia, and canaries come from the Canary Islands, where a greenish-yellow breed lives.

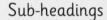

Song
Budgies make a loud squawking sound but can usually learn to talk. The canary is the best singer of all the birds that are kept as pets.

Handling your pet
Budgies can be handled more easily than canaries. In fact, they seem to like sitting on a finger or shoulder. They also like to fly around the room, so make sure they can't fly into or onto a fire.

Pictures give important information too

Feeding
Both budgies and canaries eat seed as well as some green plants. Both have strong bills for cracking hard seed for the kernels. All birds need clean water all the time.

Think about it

1. What is the main heading of the page from the information book?
2. The first sub-heading is 'Where they come from'. Write the other sub-headings.

Now try these

1. Make a list of reasons for keeping a dog as a pet, and make another list of the problems.

2. Make a list of the reasons for keeping a cat as a pet, and make another list of the problems.

3. Write a report about keeping a dog **or** a cat as a pet. Do it like the one about keeping pet birds. You might use these sub-headings if you wish:

Feeding your pet   Keeping your pet clean
Exercising your pet   Fun with your pet

Making notes

It is helpful to make notes when using information books.

This page is from an information book about bears.

Chapter title

Polar bears

Key words are underlined

The frozen sea around the <u>North Pole</u> is polar bear country. The bears <u>live</u> at the <u>edge of the ice</u>, where it meets the sea.

Sub-heading

Good swimmers

The polar bears have strong, partly webbed front paws, which help make them good swimmers. They can stay under water for up to two minutes.

Pictures give important information too

Hunters

Each bear needs to catch and eat one seal every 11 days. It will sit for hours next to a seals' breathing hole in the ice, waiting for one to come up for air. Then it will pounce. These bears also eat seabirds, fish and crabs.

Think about it

1. Make a list of the sub-headings in the report.
2. The key words have been underlined in the first paragraph. Write them in your book.

Now try these

1. Write the sub-heading for each paragraph of the information about polar bears. Next to it write the key words.
2. Use your key words to write some sentences of your own about polar bears. Close the book before you start.
3. At the bottom of this page is a paragraph about pandas. Make a list of the key words, then close the book and write the story in your own words.

There is an ancient Chinese legend that tells why Giant Pandas are marked black and white. Long ago they were white, like polar bears. One day they went to a funeral of a young girl. They had put ashes on their arms as a sign that they felt sad. They were crying bitterly. They wiped their eyes to dry the tears. They hugged themselves in sorrow. They covered their ears with their paws to block out the sound of weeping. Wherever they touched themselves, the ashes stained their fur black.

Thinking about books

At school and at home we often read or look at books.
Here are some book covers.

2 — The Littlest Dragon Gets the Giggles — Title — Publisher — Margaret Ryan and Jamie Smith — Collins Yellow Storybook

1 — An Alphabet of DINOSAURS — Author — Illustrator — BY PETER DODSON · PAINTINGS BY WAYNE D. BARLOWE

3 — Pets — Amanda Benjamin — COLLINS FIRSTS

4 — THE OWL'S LESSON — NICK BUTTERWORTH

5 — Jennifer Jones Won't Leave Me Alone! — STORY BY Frieda Wishinsky — PICTURES BY Linda Hendry

Think about it

1. What information can we get just by looking at the covers?
   The first one has been done to help you.

   1 Title: An Alphabet of Dinosaurs
      Author: Peter Dodson
      Illustrator: Wayne D. Barlowe
      This book is probably about: Dinosaurs

2. Now do the same thing for the rest of the books.

Now try these

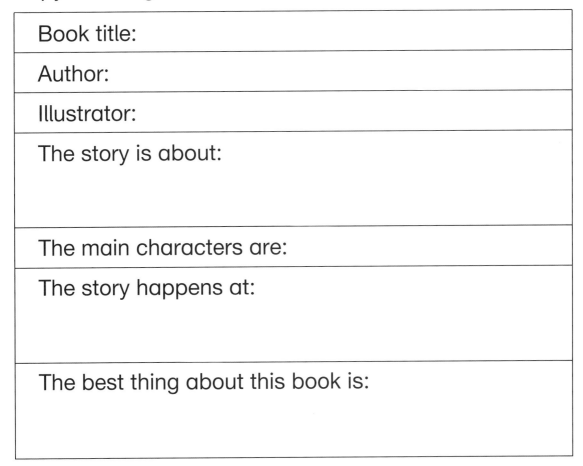

1. Choose a storybook you like.
   Copy this diagram and fill in the answers.

Book title:
Author:
Illustrator:
The story is about:
The main characters are:
The story happens at:
The best thing about this book is:

2. For this activity, choose an information book you have used. Copy this diagram and fill in the answers.

Book title:
Author:
Illustrator:
The book is about:
The best thing about this book is:
The worst thing about this book is: